D0854785

First published in the UK in 2009 by Little Star Creations,
an imprint of Holland Publishing PLC.
18 Bourne Court, Southend Road,
Woodford Green, Essex, IG8 8HD.

www.littlestarcreations.co.uk

Copyright © 2009 Lavish Productions. All rights reserved.
No part of this publication may be reproduced, stored in a retrieval
system, or transmitted in any form or by any means, electronic,
mechanical, photocopying, recording or otherwise, without the prior
permission of the copyright owner.

Designed by: Lavish Productions

Printed in China

Cute little rhymes full of

giggles

he t Poets Club™

The Pet Poets Club™

To all our lovely owners
Who think that we can't speak
Who think we only bark and growl
Miaow, or squawk, or squeak

We do indeed have voices
We use them all the time
At the legendary Pet Poets Club
The home of rhythm and rhyme

Cute little rhymes...
for those special times

GIGGLES

I felt I really had to say

I think about you every day

And to show how much you mean to me

Here's some very cute pet poetry

An amazing little creature

Lives here within this house

It's 'now you see him, now you don't'

The vanishing MAGIC MOUSE!

I watch his head pop out of his hole

I see his little ears

But before I get my chance to pounce

He goes and DISAPPEARS!

I don't know what
you're laughing at!
Have you never seen a Pom
in a bright
YELLOW HAT?

What could be merrier...

Than a cute,

dancing terrier?

Tuh-wit, tuh-woo

It's strange but true

And everyone laughs when I tell it...

...Tuh-wit, tuh-woo

Instead of a pooh...

I regurgitate a pellet!

I remember I'm a goldfish
And that's about the lot
I know I swim in water
But water...hmmm...is what?

I think I live inside a bowl
I've forgotten how I know
Somebody must have told me
A long, long time ago

I'm sure I'm here all on my own
Of that I'm fairly clear
'Oh, good morning George, nice day for it"
I'd forgotten he was here!

How come you never seem to age

Despite the passing years?

And the only things that seem to sag

Are your big, long floppy ears!

Oh my god it's freezing!
Must I really go outside?
It's surely 50 degrees below
I think it's time to hide!

I know I've got a nice fur coat
But even so, I'll freeze
So I'd rather stay right here indoors
Oh let me...pretty please!!!

Ooh-arghh-eek-ouch-ooh-arghh-YEOWWW!

I really wish I hadn't said that I would do this now!

Eek-arghh-oh-oh-ooh-ouch-STREWTH!

Someone bet me that I wouldn't walk across this roof!

Ouch-oh-ooh-eek-argh-argh-OOOH!

Now I realise it is quite a stupid thing to do!

Argh-oh-ooh-ooh-OH MY WORD, THE PAIN!

There's no way on Earth I'm ever gonna

walk on that again!

A cat in a hat

How funny is that?

You may not be that fast

But you've sure got the moves

So let's party on down

To some cool, funky grooves

Poetry in slow motion

I like to take things slowly...
...Is there any other way?
If you take everything slow
Then you'll always know...

...you'll have plenty to do the next day!

It wasn't me that did it
Just look at my innocent face!
I was busy being somewhere else
And nowhere near the place!

I'm sorry someone trod in it
And caused that dreadful mess
But it absolutely wasn't me
I have nothing to confess

There's no proof I'm the culprit
The evidence is slim
And check out the size of that cat next door!
Why don't you interrogate him?!

Shiver me timbers!
Pieces of eight!
The Pussycat Pirates are here!
We're hoisting the mainsail
(Whatever that is?)
So it's time to start shaking with fear!

The Terrible Tabbies
That's what we be called
And right now, our lips we be licking
We're after the treasure
(That you call a roast)
We be going to steal your chicken!

There's nothing as funny

As a big, sulky bunny!

I really love my glam long hair
But I just can't take it anywhere!

Getting caught in the rain makes it go all frizzy
And I end up looking blonde and dizzy

Spending time in the sun makes it dry and brittle
A nightmare when you're really little

If I go out on a windy day
The look I get is ... flyaway!

...And worse than that, it goes all knotty
Which frankly drives me rather dotty

...And it takes forever to comb it through
Honestly, what's a girl to do?

Have you ever seen a pussycat waltz?
Well now you'll get your chance
It isn't every day you see
A cat that loves to dance

I can tango, salsa and rumba
Man, I love that Latin flair!
Or glide across the hallway floor
Like a feline Fred Astaire

This stuff smells really groovy man
I'm starting to feel a bit trippy
I think this is the bit where I suddenly change...
...into the Cat-Nippy Hippy

I could drone on about it for hours
Some say that I sound evangelic
Please don't think I'm boring or hooked on the stuff
I just love that it's so psychedelic

I want to win this Dog Show
If I don't, I won't stop barking
So make sure those judges know it
Before they start their marking

I'd better win this Dog Show
I'm by far the prettiest here
Someone's ankles will get bitten
If I don't come first this year!

Tally Ho, it's Bertie here!
A true, blue-blooded Beagle
With my stately gait and pedigree
I'm positively regal!

I really am a class above
Lord of all that I survey
And I have to say I'll be very miffed
If I don't come first today

So Toodle Pip, it's been nice to chat
But alas, I have to go
And win yet another 'Best in Class'
Here's to a jolly good show!

Where's my spring?

I'm a little Springer Spaniel
But I seem to have no spring
I've had a good look everywhere
And I can't find anything!

It's really quite frustrating
And I'm getting quite wound up
But how can that be, when there's no key
To wind this Springer up?

A Night at the Opera

I've always really wanted
To be an opera star
I know that I'd be really good
Tra, la, la, la, la, la!

My fans worldwide would love me
And throw roses at my paws
I'd blow kisses at the audience
And lap up their applause

They'd demand to have an encore
From the ultimate performer
So I'd sing my favourite aria
Poochini's, Nessun Dorma!

Tennis is my favourite thing
I'm a real fan of the sport
And it's always been my biggest dream
To play on centre court

I would practise hard and learn my shots
You would find no pupil keener
Perhaps I'd even get to play
With Venus or Serena!

I'd love to be a tennis star...
...And make a real packet
But alas it will remain a dream
As I couldn't hold a racquet!

Now you see me...now you don't!

It's now you see me now you don't
Now that's a clever trick!
So it makes me laugh when humans say
That Dalmatians are all thick!

One minute I'm as clear as day
Then I've disappeared from view!
If humans were as bright as me
They'd be able to do this too!

Why is it so cold in here?
Have they never heard of heating?
My food bowl is always empty!
Have they never heard of eating?

Every time I have a stretch
Somebody rubs my belly!
Oh why can't I be left in peace
To sit and watch the telly?

Donny's Disco Night

Get on down and meet the pack
Who'll make you feel alright
Then shake that tail and wave those paws
At Donnie's Disco Night

You'll feel yourself get carried away
When the joint is really jumping
But remember the rule (or they'll throw you out)
It's strictly 'No leg humping!'

You may have heard about these two
We call them the terrible twins
They may look sweet, but secretly...
They get up to terrible things

Yapping after all the boys
Staying out all hours of night
Wearing clothes that are far too short
And getting caught up in a fight

We won't go into details
About their bad-girl capers
Though you're bound to find out anyway...
...when you read it in the papers!

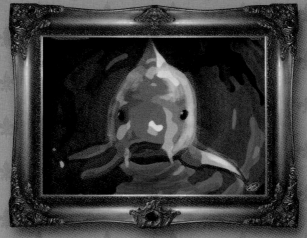

A NOT-SO-KOI CARP

A not-so-Koi Carp

Did you know I'm worth a mint
I bet you would never have guessed
Ten thousand quid at the very last count
Now admit it, you're really impressed

Some lesser fish think it's vulgar
To be worth so much lovely cash
But bully to them, if they want to be poor
What's wrong with a fish being flash?

I know I look sweet

But I'm really a sinner

And the second you're gone

I'm stealing your dinner!

Thirty seven pumpkin seeds

I can fit inside my cheeks

And here's the really clever thing

I can keep them there for weeks!

The tango...the rumba

The cha-cha-cha

I'm a strictly teeny

Ball room star!

The
Pet Poets
Club™

It's time for us to say goodbye

We thank you for your time

And hope to see you back again

At the home of rhythm and rhyme

Titles in the series:

Cute little rhymes about **love**

Cute little rhymes about **Friendship**

Cute little rhymes for **new baby**

Cute little rhymes for **dad**

Cute little rhymes for **mum**

Cute little rhymes for **grandma**

Cute little rhymes full of **giggles**

Cute little rhymes about **memories**

Cute little rhymes about **wisdom**

© Copyright Lavish Rights 2009